MY BEDTIME NURSERY RHYME BOOK

Emily Hunter

HARVEST HOUSE PUBLISHERS
EUGENE, OREGON 97402

Blessings on thee, little lamb,
Where'er thy feet may take thee.

God in Heaven is watching thee,
And He will not forsake thee!

Blessings on thee, little lamb!
Be glad and never fear.

Your loving Keeper is the Lord,
And He is ever near!

MY BEDTIME NURSERY RHYME BOOK

By Emily Hunter
With Illustrations by the Author

Library of Congress Catalog Card Number 86-080708
ISBN 0-89081-890-8

Printed in Korea

HARVEST HOUSE PUBLISHERS
EUGENE, OREGON 97402

To know God is to love Him . . .

To love Him is to praise Him!

TABLE OF CONTENTS

OTHER BOOKS BY THE AUTHOR: The Bible-Time Nursery Rhyme Book
Christian Charm Course — Man In Demand

I Praise You Because You Have Always Been

"From everlasting to everlasting thou art God" (Psalm 90:2).

I am six, and Bill is eight,
  And sister Jane is five.
That's the way we count the years
  That we have been alive.

How old is God? He has no age!
  He's not like you or me,
For God has always, always been,
  And He will always be!

When is your birthday? Does every person have a birthday?
Does God have a birthday?

You Made the Sun to Give Us Light

"Thou hast prepared the light and the sun" (Psalm 74:16).

How glad I am each morning
  When I see the sun appear.
He smiles at me...
  I smile right back...
  I say, "I'm glad you're here!"

How glad I am that God above
  Is full of power and might.
Who else could make
    the sun come up
Each day to give me light?

Why is the boy smiling? Who makes the sun come up each morning?
Some mornings we cannot see the sun. Is it still there? What is it hiding behind?

11

You Fill the Oceans with Water

"The Lord made the sea" (Exodus 20:11).

I'm dipping up the ocean!
 I'll dip the ocean dry!
No, my darling! No, you can't!
 No matter how you try!

God keeps filling oceans
 With water to the brim.
The oceans never go away.
 They stay because of Him.

What is the boy trying to do? Can he empty the ocean? Who keeps the ocean filled with water?

You Formed Great Mountains

"He that formeth the mountains...
the LORD is his name"
(Amos 4:13).

I built a mountain out of sand.
  I shaped it carefully by hand.

A wave came in that very day
  And washed my mountain all away!

God made mountains
  tall and grand,
Rising high at
  His command.

My mountain didn't
  last a day, but
God's great mountains
  stay and stay!

Point to the boy who is frowning. Why is he unhappy?
Point to the boy who is gazing at the tall mountains. Can you guess what he is thinking?

You Made Birds of Every Kind

"God created every winged fowl" (Genesis 1:21).

The owl said, "Whoo...
    Who made you?"
Said the crow,
    "I don't know!"

Said Bill Blue,
    "I know who!
God made me,
    And God made you!"

Said the owl,
    "True...true!"
And away he flew
With a loud
    "Whooo....whooo...!"

Can you name other birds God made? What is your favorite bird?

14

You Made the Wind

"He that createth the wind...the Lord is his name"(Amos 4:13).

Wind, wind!
   I can't see you!
You are hidden
   From my sight!
I can't see you,
   But I feel you,
Tugging, tugging
   At my kite!

Wind, wind!
   I can't see you,
But I know that
   You are there!
I can't see you,
   But I feel you,
Twirling, swirling
   Through my hair!

Wind, wind!
   Who has made you?
Who has made you
   Twirl and blow?
God above—'tis He
   Who made you!
For the Bible
   Tells me so!

*"He causeth his wind to
   blow" (Psalm 147:18).*

Have you ever seen the wind?
   How do you know it is there?
     What is the wind doing for this boy?

15

You Send the Seasons Every Year

"While the earth remaineth, seed time and harvest, summer and winter shall not cease" (Genesis 8:22).

"Will summer come this year?"
  asked Jane,
    Looking through the window pane.

"All I see is rain, rain, rain!
  Every day is just the same!"

"Summer's coming, daughter dear!
  God has promised. Never fear!

"What He's promised, He will do,
  For we know His Word is true.

"Winter, spring...then summer, fall...
  Every year God sends them all.

"Yes, my daughter...never fear!
  Summer time will come
    this year!"

What do you especially like about the summer time?
Who sends us summer every year?

You Made Trees for Us

"Out of the ground made the LORD God to grow every tree" (Genesis 2:9).

A tree house! A tree house! I love to be in my tree house!
  I'm looking here...I'm looking there...I'm looking all around!

A tree house! A tree house! I love to be in my tree house!
  I am so high...up in the sky...I'm far above the ground!

I feel so close to God up here, away up in this tree!
  I say to God, "You made this tree! You made it just for me!"

A tree house! A tree house! I love to be in my tree house!
  I say to God, "I love you so! And you love me, I truly know!

    You made this tree...and you made me!
      That's why I praise you so!"

Would you like to live in a world with no trees at all anywhere?
Can you look out your window and see a tree?
Are you glad God made that tree?

18

You've Given Us Fruit to Eat

"And God said, Let the earth bring forth the fruit tree yielding fruit"

(Genesis 1:11).

I love apples!
I love cherries!
I love peaches,
    pears and
        berries!

When I taste
A purple plum,
I lick my lips
    and say,
      "YUM, YUM!"

What kind of fruit is the boy eating? Do you think he is saying "yum, yum"?

What other kinds of fruit does God give us to eat?

19

You Know Every Star in the Sky

"He telleth the number of the stars;
he calleth them all by their names"
(Psalm 147:4).

I can't count the stars...can you?
  That's too hard for me to do!

God can count them everywhere,
  For He's the One who put them there!

Some are great, and some are small,
  And some we cannot see at all!

Only God knows every star,
  Knows exactly where they are!

Knows their name and number, too!
  That's not hard for Him to do.

God knows all there is to know!
  That is why I praise Him so!

What is the boy trying to do?
Will he be able to count all the stars?
Who knows how many stars are in the sky?

You Do Marvelous Things!

"Great and marvelous are thy works, Lord God Almighty" (Revelation 15:3).
"Thou art the God that doeth wonders" (Psalm 77:14).

Pretty bluebird in the sky,
　　Who taught you to fly so high?
God taught me to fly so high,
　　Said the bluebird in the sky.

*Praise Him, children,
　　when you see
Bluebirds flying high
　　like me!*

Pretty flowers that gaily bloom,
　　Who gave you your sweet perfume?
God gave us our sweet perfume,
　　Said the flowers that gaily bloom.

*Praise Him, children,
　　everywhere,
When our perfume
　　fills the air!*

Robin, sitting in your nest,
    Who gave you your bright red breast?
God gave me my bright red breast
    Said the robin in the nest.

Praise Him, children,
    when you see
Brightly colored birds
    like me!

Mr. Mole, so fat and round,
    Who taught you to dig in the ground?
God taught me to dig in the ground,
    Said the mole so fat and round.

Praise Him, children,
    when you see
A mole that's digging
    just like me!

23

Mommy cat with paws
    like mittens,
Who taught you to carry
    your kittens?

God taught me to carry
    my kittens,
Said the cat with paws
    like mittens.

Praise Him, children,
    when you see
A loving mommy cat
    like me!

Busy Mr. Beaver-Sam,
    Who taught you to build your dam?
God taught me to build my dam,
    Answered Mr. Beaver-Sam.

    Praise Him, children,
        when you see
    A beaver building dams like me!

Said the owl with big round eyes,
    Listen, children! I am wise!
All we are, and all we know
    Comes from God who made us so!

What did God teach the mole to do? the mommy cat? the beaver? the bluebird?
Who gave the flowers their fragrance, and the robin its red breast?

You Know Every Hair on my Head

"The very hairs of your head are all numbered" (Matthew 10:30).

Hippety-hop!
  Hippety-hop!
Here I go
  To the barber shop!

I sit me down
  Into the chair.
The barber starts
  To cut my hair.

Clippety-clip!
  Clippety-clip!
The scissors go
  A-snippety-snip!

Look at my hair
  All over the floor!
But I know God will
  Grow me some more!

Skippety-hop!
  Skippety-hop!
Here I go home
  from the
    barber shop!

The Bible tells me
  That Jesus said
That God knows
  Every hair on
    my head!

It's great to know
  That God is aware —
Of boys like me —
  And even their hair!

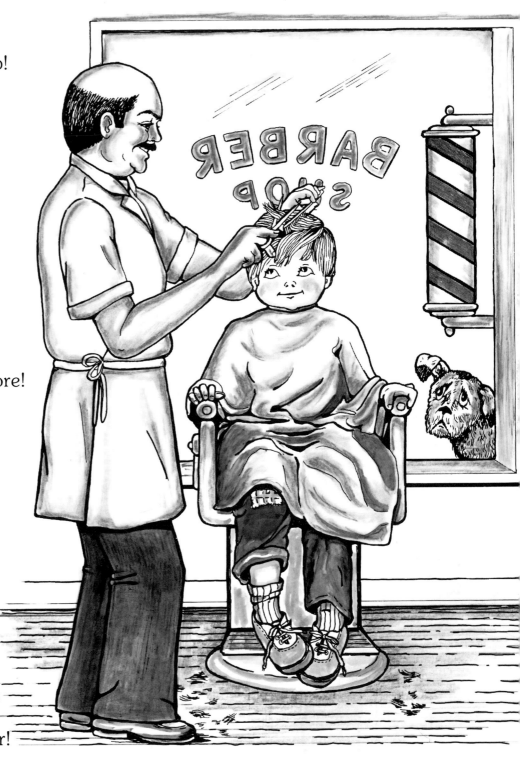

Do you know how many hairs there are on your head?
Is there someone who knows?

You've Made Our Wonderful Hands

*"Know ye that the LORD,
it is he that hath made us"*
(Psalm 100:3).

Look at my fingers!
   Look at my thumb!
Listen and hear
   What they have done!
They've buttoned my vest,
   And helped me get dressed,
And "Rat-a-tum-tum!"
   They've played on my drum!

See how my fingers
   "Tappety-tap"!
And if I am glad,
   They "clappety-clap"!
Whatever I say
   They quickly obey!
And when I am tired,
   They rest in my lap!

Look at my fingers!
   Five on each hand!
They will do anything
   That I command!
My hands are so odd —
   But they're made by God !
But just how He made them,
   I can't understand!

What do your hands do for you when you are hungry?
When you look through a picture book?
When your nose itches? Who made your hands?

26

You See Us Wherever We May Be

"The eyes of the Lord are in every place" (Proverbs 15:3).

How I love to play hide and seek!
   I hide behind the chair.
I hold real still and make no noise,
   So no one knows I'm there.

But God, your eyes see everything!
   You see me everywhere!
You even see me when I hide
   Behind my Daddy's chair!

Where is the girl hiding? Can the boy see her behind the chair? Who does see her there?

"Can any hide that I shall not see him? saith the Lord" (Jeremiah 23:24).

You See Us Big or Small

"Thou God seest me"
(Genesis 16:13).

God looks down from heaven.
He sees us one and all.
He sees us if we're big,
He sees us if we're small.

He sees the great big elephant,
As big as any house!
But God looks down and also sees
The tiny little mouse!

It matters not to God above
How little we may be!
There's no one in the whole wide world
Too small for Him to see!

Does God see big "grown up" people? Does God see little children? Does God see tiny babies, too?

And God. . .You Never Sleep!

"He that keepeth thee will not slumber (Psalm 121:3). "I will both lay me down in peace, and sleep: for thou, LORD, makest me dwell in safety" (Psalm 4:8).

Little bear says, "Mama dear,
   Does God in Heaven sleep?"
"No," she says, "He's always there
   To watch and guard and keep."

Mama bear says, "Never fear
   When I turn out the light.
God is watching over you
   Throughout the dark of night!"

When you sleep at Grandma's house, does God know where you are?

Does He watch over you there, too?

29

You Watch Over Us

"He careth for you" (I Peter 5:7).

Baby Sue! Baby Sue!
  Sister's watching over you!
She'll not leave you all alone,
  Lest you fall upon a stone.
Sister's watching there nearby,
  Lest you stub your toe and cry!

Baby Sue! Baby Sue!
  Someone else is watching, too!
God is watching everywhere.
  You are always in His care!
Just as we all care for you,
  God in Heaven loves you, too!

Why is big sister watching over Baby Sue? Who else is watching over her?

30

You Hear Us When We Pray

"My God will hear me" (Micah 7:7).

Grandma lives far down the street.
  She lives there all alone.
When I want to talk to her,
  I call her on the phone.

I don't need
  A telephone
To talk to God
  Each day!

When I want
  To talk to Him,
I close my eyes
  And pray!

Who is the girl talking to on the telephone?
Who is she talking to as she kneels beside her bed?
Do we need a telephone to talk to God? Can God hear us even when we whisper?

31

You Made All Creatures — And My Pets, Too!

"All things were made by him" (John 1:3).

I have a pretty kitty,
  And when I stroke her fur,
An engine deep inside of her
  Goes "PURR...PURR...PURR"!

I have a yellow birdie.
  My birdie's name is Pete.
And when I say "hello" to him,
  He answers, "TWEET! TWEET!"

I have a little puppy.
   My puppy's name is Jiggles.
And every time I call his name,
   His little tail wiggles!

I have a little pony.
   I feed him oats and hay.
And when he sees me coming,
   He goes, "NEIGH! NEIGH!"

I love my friendly little pets,
   As you can plainly see,
For God has made each one of them
   And given them to me!

What kind of pets does the girl have? Who made each one of her pets?

33

You Help Us To Grow

"Thou hast granted me life" (Job 10:12).

See this mark upon the wall?
  Daddy says I'm growing tall!
See this mark away down here?
  That's how tall I was last year!
See my feet? They're growing, too!
  Take a look at that big shoe!

Though it may not always show,
  Every single day I grow.
God gives food for me to eat.
  Then my bones grow — and my feet!
Though I'm just a little lad,
  Someday I'll be as big as Dad!

What is the boy looking at? Is he happy to see how much he has grown?

You Give Us the Food We Eat

"Give thanks unto the LORD; who gives food to all flesh" (Psalm 136:25).

There once was a bunny by the name of Jake.
One day he said, "What shall I make?"

"I know what I'll make! I'll make a cake
   And put it in the oven to bake and bake!"
But then the bunny by the name of Jake
   Said, "What will I need to make my cake?"

"I'll need some butter, and I'll need some milk,
And I'll need some flour that is soft as silk.
I'll need some eggs, and I'll need some honey —"
So off went the happy little bunny.

He hopped away on his little legs
To the chicken house to get two eggs.

The hen said, "I've laid eggs for you,
   For God has said that's what I'm to do!"

"Thank you, hen!" said Bunny Jake.
   "These eggs will help me make my cake!"

He went to the miller
    That very same hour,
And said, "Can you grind
    Some grain into flour?"

The miller said, "Yes, I have lots of grain,
For God sent the sun and He sent the rain!"

"Thank you, miller!" said Bunny Jake.
    "This flour will help me make my cake!"

And then he went to some busy bees.
   He said, "Can you spare some honey, please?"
    "Yes," said the bees,
     "That's within our power,
      For God puts sweetness
      In each flower!"

"Thank you, bees!" said Bunny Jake.
   "This honey will help me make my cake!"

He went to the cow with her big round udder.
He said, "Please give me some milk and butter!"

The cow said, "Yes, I can fill your need,
For God's given grass on which I feed!
My milk is rich. You can take the cream
And make the best butter ever seen!"

"Thanks for milk and butter!" said Jake.
"Dear cow, you've helped me make my cake!"

And then the bunny
By the name of Jake
Had all he needed
To make his cake.

He had his butter.
He had his milk.
He had his flour ground
Soft as silk.

He had all the honey
That he might need,
And two big eggs
That were fresh
indeed!

He mixed and mixed
And stirred and stirred,
And then without
Another word,
He put it in the oven
So it could bake,

And after a while —
OUT CAME A CAKE!

He called to his friends, "You come and eat!
    Just see what I've made! A cake so sweet!"
When Jake's good friends all came to see,
    The proud bunny said, "Just look at ME!"

"Who else in the world but GREAT BUNNY JAKE
    Could be so great as to make this cake!"
But as the bunny was puffed with pride,
    Just who do you think ran up to his side?

Here came the miller and the cow, if you please!
Here came the hen! And here came the bees!
They said, "We heard you, Bunny Jake!
We heard you bragging about your cake!"

"But we want all your friends to know
'Twas God who made the grain to grow!
God gave the cow her milk and cream!
God gave the grass she ate, so green!
God gave the bees the flowers, so sweet!
And God gave the hens the eggs we eat!"

When Jake heard all the words they said,
  He answered, "Friends, let's bow our head!
Before we even take one bite,
  Let's thank the Lord, for this is right!"

And all Jake's friends who gathered there
  Bowed heads and closed their eyes in prayer.
"We thank you, God!" prayed Bunny Jake.
  — And then his friends all ate their cake!

*When mother buys a can of soup at the grocery store and serves it for lunch,
  should we thank God for it? Why?*

47

You Give Us Much to Be Thankful For

"Be thankful unto him" (Psalm 100:4).

I wrote a "thank-you" note today
   To my dear Grandma Lee,
To thank her for the birthday gift
   That she had sent to me.

And then I wrote another note
   To thank my Aunty Lou.
And then I wrote to
   Grandma Jones
To tell her "thank you," too.

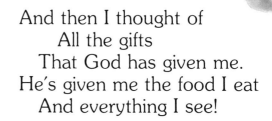

And then I thought of
   All the gifts
   That God has given me.
He's given me the food I eat
   And everything I see!

And so I wrote a "thank-you" note
   To God in Heaven above,
   And signed it, "From your
   Little child,
     Rebecca Jane,
     With love!"

When someone gives you a gift, what do you say? If you were to write a "thank-you"
note to God today, what would you thank Him for? Can you name 3 things?

You Give Us Happy Thanksgiving Times

"It is a good thing to give thanks unto the LORD" (Psalm 92:1).

Everyone's here!
There's laughter and
  chatter!
Out in the kitchen
Dishes a-clatter!
See the big turkey!
If it were fatter,
It wouldn't fit
On mother's big platter!

Now we're all seated
Next to each other.
Dad's at the head,
And I'm next to brother.
Next comes my sis,
And then my dear
  mother.
(Oh, she is sweet!
Oh, how I love her!)

Everything's ready!
The table is spread!
Everyone's still.
We each bow our head.
We thank God for
  blessings!
We thank Him for bread!
And now we all eat,
For the blessing is said!

Point to the father and the mother. Where are grandma and grandpa seated?
What special day is it? What do we do on Thanksgiving Day?

49

You Are Our Good Shepherd

"The LORD is my shepherd; I shall not want" (Psalm 23:1).

The Lord is my shepherd.
 I am His little lamb.
His eye is always on me.
 He knows just where I am.

He leads me by still waters.
 By pleasant streams I rest.
He guides me in the right path.
 The one He knows is best.

When wolves are all around me,
 His rod and staff I see,
To keep me from all danger,
 To guard and comfort me.

And though I walk through valleys
 Where shadows dark may be,
I still will not be fearful,
 For He is there with me.

What do shepherds do? Are the lambs safe as long as they stay by their shepherd?
Does the Lord care for you just like a shepherd cares for his sheep?

You Love All Children Everywhere

"Let the little children come unto me...And he took them up in his arms, put his hands upon them, and blessed them" (Mark 10:14, 16).

Jesus loves the Eskimo
  Who lives up north
    In cold and snow.

And Indian children
  Smiling sweet
    With moccasins
      Upon their feet.

And children who
  Have slanted eyes—
    The Orientals,
      Small in size.

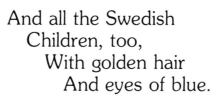

And all the Swedish
  Children, too,
    With golden hair
      And eyes of blue.

He loves the Dutch,
  So clean and neat
    With wooden shoes
      Upon their feet.

He loves the Scottish
  Lass and lad,
    Who wear their skirts
      Of Scottish plaid.

He loves all children
  Dark or fair.
    He loves all children
      EVERYWHERE!

Does Jesus love you, too?

You Put Love in Our Hearts for Others

"Let us love one another: for love is of God" (I John 4:7).

I made a valentine today.
  I made it for my mother.
I drew a great big heart to say
  How dearly that I love her.

I colored it with color crayons
  And pasted lace around it.
I placed it by the mailbox,
  And waited till she found it.

I waited and I waited,
    Till she came to get the mail.
At last I saw her coming,
    Slowly walking down the trail.

And when she found the valentine,
    She said, "What can this be?
Did someone really send this
    Pretty valentine to me?"

And when she paused beside the post,
    I jumped out from behind it!
I said, "Oh, Mommy dearest!
    I thought you'd never find it!"

She said, "I love my valentine!
    How nicely you have drawn it!
With roses red and violets blue,
    And lacy ruffles on it!"

And then she hugged me close to her,
    And said, "Dear child of mine,
How good of you to show me love
    With this sweet valentine!"

What did the girl make for her mother? Where did she place it? Was her mother happy to receive it?
God has given us hearts that can feel love for one another. Tell someone today, "I love you!"

You Heal Our Bruises and Hurts

"I am the LORD that healeth thee" (Exodus 15:26).

Tommy fell and skinned his knee.
    His knee was red and sore.
        He prayed,
    "Dear God, please give me skin
        Just like I had before!"

One day he took his bandage off.
  He shouted, "Come and see!
My God has grown me brand new skin
  Upon my poor red knee!

"How great of God to heal my skin!
  How great a God is He!
Who else in all the world could grow
  New skin upon my knee?"

What happened to Tommy? Have you ever skinned your knee? What did mother do?
We cleanse and bandage our bruises to help them get well, but we can't make new skin grow.
Who is the only One who can do that?

You Give Us Smiles to Wear on Our Faces

"Thou hast put gladness in my heart" (Psalm 4:7).

Where do happy children live?
   They live in Happy-ville,
Where birdies sing and children swing,
   And daisies dance on the hill!

The happy children smile all day.
   Their faces wear no frowns.
For every child loves to obey,
   And happiness abounds.

Where do grumpy children live?
   They live in Grumpy-town,
Where grumpies fret and pout and cry,
   And smiles are upside down!

Their dogs are sad! Their cats are mad!
   And the flowers hang their head!
For never once in Grumpy-town
   Is a kind word ever said!

Where do you want to live and play?
   If you pout and fret and frown,
You'll have to spend the live-long day
   With the grumpies in Grumpy-town!

But if you choose
   The happy way—
And you can,
   If you simply will—
      Then you can smile
         And laugh all day
            With the children
               In Happy-ville!

Point to each child in Happy-ville. Do you see any frowning faces? Point to each child in Grumpy-town.
Do you see even one smiling face? Which town does God want you to live in?

57

You Show Us That Doing Right Makes Us Happy

"Happy is that people, whose God is the LORD" (Psalm 144:15).

Happiness comes in blue,
Happiness comes in pink.

Happiness comes in doing dishes
At the kitchen sink.

Happiness comes in orange,
Happiness comes in red.

Happiness comes in taking Mother
Breakfast in her bed!

Happiness comes in yellow,
   Happiness comes in green.
Happiness comes in church
   With Mom and Dad, and me between!

Happiness comes in lavender.
   It comes in purple, too.
Happiness comes in doing
   Just what God has told us to!

"He that keepeth the law, happy is he"
               (Proverbs 29:18).

"My heart is glad"
   (Psalm 16:9).

What did the girl and boy do to please their mother? What did the family do together to please God?

You Give Us Grandmas to Love

"How sweet are thy words unto my taste!" (Psalm 119:103).

I love my grandma's cookies.
   She makes them just for me.
And when she's finished baking them,
   She holds me on her knee.

She reads me Bible stories.
   The stories are all true.
I dearly love my grandma!
   I love her cookies, too!

Do you like to eat freshly baked cookies? Do you like to hear Bible stories?
Are you thankful for grandmas?

You Teach Us to be Thoughtful of Others

"Be ye kind one to another"
(Ephesians 4:32).

When Timmy entered the living room,
  With Grandma close behind,
He said, "I'll grab the softest chair—
  The first one that I find!"

So Timmy quickly settled down
  Into the only chair,
And left his poor old grandma
  Sadly standing there.

62

Thoughtful little Jimmy knew
  That Jesus said, "Be kind."
And so he jumped up from his chair,
  And said, "Oh, please take mine!"

And poor, tired old Grandma
  Smiled at Jimmy happily.
She sat down in the chair—and then
  Took Jimmy on her knee!

Which boy was kind to his grandma? Which boy looks happy?
Which boy made his grandma look happy, too?

63

You Give Us Songbirds to Cheer Us

"The time of the singing of birds is come" (Song of Solomon 2:12).

A little bird was sitting
    Upon the window sill,
And looking through the window,
    He smiled at little Jill.

"Little Jill," the birdie said,
    "Why do you look so sad?
I'll sing a pretty song for you,
    And it will make you glad!"

"Chirp...chirp! Trill...trill!"
    The birdie sang a song for Jill.
"Chirp...chirp! Tweet...tweet!"
    The song he sang was very sweet.

The bird looked through the window
    Again at little Jill.
She said, "Oh, little birdie,
    I felt so very ill,
But you have cheered me greatly...
    I know the Scriptures tell
That if I have a merry heart,
    'Twill help me to get well!"

"Chirp...chirp! Trill...trill!"
    Again the birdie sang for Jill.
"Chirp...chirp! Tweet...tweet!"
    Again his song was very sweet.

Little Jill began to smile.
    She was no longer sad.
She said, "Dear little birdie,
    Your song has made me glad.
I thank the Lord in Heaven,
    Who's given you your song,
For now I shall feel better
    The whole day long!"

What was wrong with little Jill? What cheered her? Does it make you feel happy to hear birds singing?
The Bible says, "A merry heart doeth good like medicine" (Proverbs 17:22).
Does medicine help us to get well? Yes—and so does a merry heart!

You Teach Us to be Happy Helpers

"By love serve one another" (Galatians 5:13).

"Mother, what can I do for you?
Asked little Robin Red-breast."

"I'll bring you breakfast on a tray,
So you can get some bed-rest!"

"Mother, what can I do for you?"
Asked Pussie Lillie-Lou.

"I'll peel some vegetables and make
A kettle full of stew!"

"Mother, what can I do for you?"
  Asked Melanie the Mouse.

"I'll dust and sweep the dirty floors,
  And tidy up the house!"

"Mother, I just want to sit!"
  Said Grouchy Kangaroo.

And so he didn't help a bit,
  But sat the whole day through.

Now tell me, children,
  Who you think
Was happiest that day?
  The lazy kangaroo or those
    Who helped in every way?

Point to the ones who were happy.
  Can you tell their names?
    What can you do today to be happy?

67

You Teach Us to Work As Well As Play

"In all labour there is profit" (Proverbs 14:23).

"Peter, Peter!
   Paint my fence!
I'll gladly pay you
   Fifty cents!"

"No, Mr. Jones,
   I can't today!
Today I want to
   Run and play!"

"Peter, Peter!
   Scrub my floor!
I'll pay you twenty
   Cents or more!"

"No, Mrs. Brown,
   I can't today!
Today I want to
   Run and play!"

"Peter, Peter!
    Weed my yard!
I'll pay you a dollar,
    For it is hard!"

"No, Mrs. Scott,
    I can't today!
Today I want to
    Run and play!"

"Peter, Peter! Come to the zoo!
    All our friends are going, too!
Of course, you know it isn't free...
    You'll need a dollar for the fee...
And twenty cents to feed the bear...
    And fifty cents for the trolley fare!"

Peter shook his head
  And sighed.
"I cannot go!"
  The sad boy cried.

"I have no money
  To pay my way,
So I'll stay home
  Alone all day!"

As Peter's friends
  Went riding by,
He waved a sad,
  Forlorn goodbye.

He cried, "Dear God!
  I'm feeling blue!"
And then God showed
  Him what to do.

He ran to the Jones'
   To paint their fence.
He worked and earned
   His fifty cents.

He went to the Browns'
   To scrub their floor.
He earned his twenty
   Cents and more.

He went to the Scotts'
To weed their yard.
He earned a dollar,
For it was hard.

And when his friends
    Came home from the zoo,
They waved and yelled,
    "We sure missed you!"

And Peter answered
    With a happy glow,
"Just wait till next time,
    THEN I'LL GO!"

What did Peter do for Mr. Jones? What did he do for Mrs. Brown?
What did he do for Mrs. Scott? Will Peter have to stay home
the next time his friends go to the zoo? Why not?

You Teach Us to be Glad Every Day

*"This is the day that the LORD hath made;
we will rejoice and be glad in it" (Psalm 118:24).*

"I wish I were happy,"
   Said Mindy Lou.
Then close by her side
   A little bird flew.

He said, "I'll tell you
   A secret true.
God wants you happy,
   And He will help you!

"Upon your face, you must
   Wear a big smile!
And you will be happy
   After a while!"

As Mindy Lou watched
   The bird fly away,
She said, "I'll try it!
   I'll smile today!

"I'll smile even though
   I am feeling blue.
I'll see if the little bird's
   Secret is true!"

So Mindy Lou made
   Her way down the street,
Smiling at all
   She happened to meet!

She smiled at the neighbor,
    Mowing his grass.
He smiled as he said,
    "Good morning, sweet lass!"

She smiled at the widow
    Who lived all alone.
She smiled at her dog
    Who lay chewing a bone.

74

She smiled at the postman,
Carrying his sack.
He said, "Howdy-do!"
And smiled right back!

She smiled at wee Willie,
Petting his cat.
And Willie called, "Mindy!
Stop, and we'll chat!"

She smiled at the grandma
  With silver grey hair.
She smiled at everyone
  Everywhere!

And each time she smiled,
  Her smile grew and grew,
Until she was smiling
  All through and through!

The whole world was filled
  With sunshine, it seemed.
For each time she smiled—
  Right back it beamed!

Then close by her side
  Again the bird flew.
He asked, "Did you find
  That my secret was true?"

And right at that moment
  Our sweet Mindy Lou
Discovered indeed
  She was no longer blue!

What did Mindy Lou do as she walked down the street?
Does God want you to smile and be happy?
Today, pretend you are Mindy Lou. Smile at everyone and
watch them smile back at you!

76

You Love Me All the Time

"I have loved thee with an everlasting love" (Jeremiah 31:3).

I look in the mirror,
  And what do I see?
I see a little girl
  Who looks like me.

    Her cheeks are pink,
      And her eyes are blue.
    I say, "Little girl!
      GOD LOVES YOU!"

I look in the mirror,
  And what do I see?
A little boy smiling,
  Just like me!

    I say, "Good morning!
      How do you do?
    It's a bright new day,
      And GOD LOVES YOU!"

I look in the mirror,
  And what do I see?
A little girl crying,
  Just like me!

    Her eyes are red,
      And she sobs, "Boo-hoo!"
    I say, "Don't cry!
      For GOD LOVES YOU!"

The next time you look in the mirror, what can you say to yourself?

I look in the mirror,
  And what do I see?
A little boy yawning,
  Just like me!

    I say, "Little boy,
      You're a sleepy-head!
    So say your prayers
      And go to bed!
    And in the morning
      The sun will shine.
    God loves you now
      And ALL THE TIME!"

You Give Us Mothers to Help Us Do Right

"Lie not one to another" (Colossians 3:9).

Cassidy, Cassidy,
　Cassidy O'Toole
Didn't like to study,
　And he didn't like school.

He woke up on a morning
　When the sun was shining bright,
And said, "This is a perfect day
　To fly my purple kite!"

"Mother dear, Mother dear!"
　Cassidy cried.
"I cannot go to school today!"
　The naughty boy lied.

"I must have eaten too much pie,
　And eaten too much cake,
For I am feeling very bad
　And have a stomach ache!"

"Cassidy, Cassidy!
Now you must stay in bed,
And you shall have no breakfast
But a crust of dry bread!

"And here's some nasty medicine
That tastes so very sour,
And here're some bitter
Pills to swallow
One every hour!"

"Mother dear, Mother dear!"
Cassidy pled.
"I think I'm feeling better...
See? My cheeks are
Turning red!

"Perhaps I'd better go to school
And study very hard,
And then when I come home,
I'll fly my kite out in the yard!"

"Cassidy, Cassidy!
It's very plain to see
That you were really never sick!
You played a trick on me!

"Now I shall have
To punish you
For such a
Naughty deed!

"As soon as you
Get home
From school,
The garden, you
Must weed!"

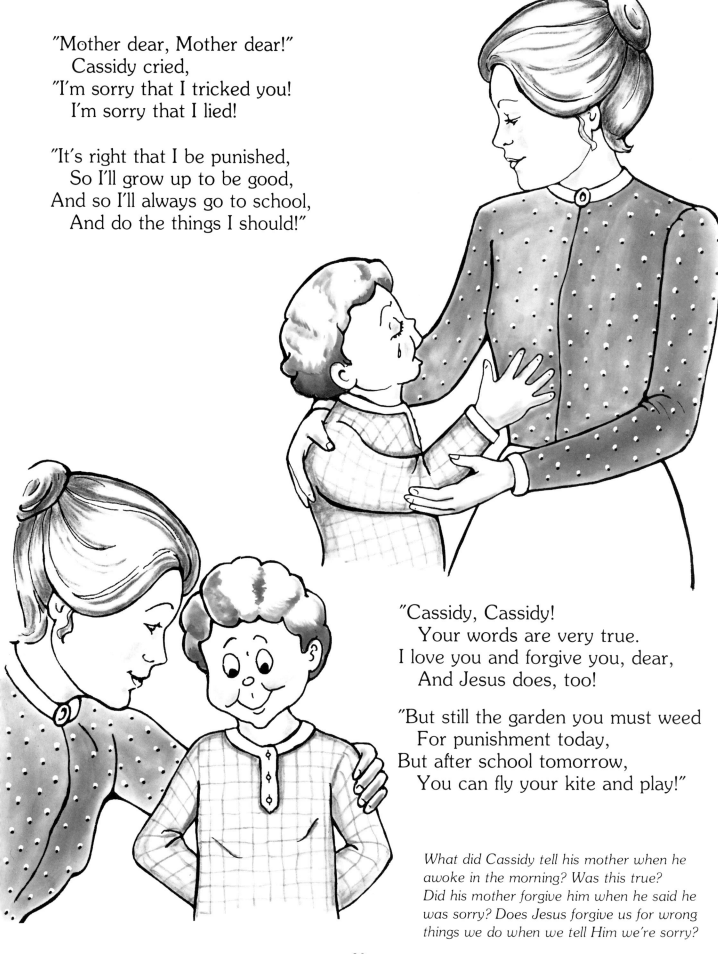

"Mother dear, Mother dear!"
  Cassidy cried,
"I'm sorry that I tricked you!
  I'm sorry that I lied!

"It's right that I be punished,
  So I'll grow up to be good,
And so I'll always go to school,
  And do the things I should!"

"Cassidy, Cassidy!
  Your words are very true.
I love you and forgive you, dear,
  And Jesus does, too!

"But still the garden you must weed
  For punishment today,
But after school tomorrow,
  You can fly your kite and play!"

*What did Cassidy tell his mother when he
awoke in the morning? Was this true?
Did his mother forgive him when he said he
was sorry? Does Jesus forgive us for wrong
things we do when we tell Him we're sorry?*

You Teach Us to Help Our Neighbors

"They helped every one his neighbor" (Isaiah 41:6).
"Thou shalt love thy neighbor as thyself" (Mark 12:31).

Poor Mrs. Jones
  Can walk no more,
But she needs food
  From the corner store.

She's old and weak.
  Her legs are lame.
She cannot walk
  Without a cane.

81

"Should I go help her?
    Of course, I should!"
Said little Mary,
    So kind and good.

And so she ran
    With her two strong legs
And brought Mrs. Jones
    Some bread and eggs.

Poor Mr. Brown,
  He's tired and old.
He needs a fire.
  His house is cold.
But he's too tired
  To gather wood.
"Should I go help him?
  Of course, I should!
I'll fill his woodbox
  Best I can,"
Said helpful, happy
  Little Dan.
And that's exactly
  What he did.
He filled his woodbox
  To the lid.

What was wrong with Mrs. Jones? What did Mary do to help her?
What was wrong with Mr. Brown? What did Dan do to help him?

83

You Give Us Things to Share With Others

"As ye would that men should do to you, do ye
also to them likewise" (Luke 6:31).

"May I swing?" asked Billy.
  "May I swing?" asked Lou.
"May I swing," asked Vicki,
  "As soon as you are through?"

"It's MY swing!" said Jan,
  "And no one swings but ME!"
So back and forth she swung and swung
  Beneath the apple tree.

"Goodbye, Jan!" said Billy.
  "Goodbye, Jan!" said Lou.

"Goodbye, Jan!" said Vicki.
  "We cannot play with you!"

As Jan was swinging
Back and forth,
Her playmates
All went home!

And selfish Jan
Sat in her swing—
Just sat there
All alone.

"Oh, please come back now, Billy!
Oh, please come back now, Lou!
Oh, please come back now, Vicki!
I'll share my swing with you!"

So Billy, Lou and Vicki
Came back to swing and play,
And Jan and all her little friends
Were happy all the day!

Does Jan look happy sitting in her swing all alone?
Does Jan look happy sharing her swing with Billy, Lou and Vicki?
Do her friends look happy, too?

You Give Us Bible Stories We Love to Hear

"Thy word have I hid in mine heart" (Psalm 119:11).

The happiest hour of the day for me
    Is when Mother holds me on her knee,
And Father sits real close beside
    And opens up the Bible wide.

And brother Jim and sister Sue
    Both gather round to join us, too.
And Father reads with his heavy voice
    Whatever story is our choice.

I love to hear the thrilling tale
    Of Jonah swallowed by the whale.
And sister Sue delights to hear
    How Jesus blessed the children dear.

The nicest part of all, I'd say,
    Is when we all hold hands and pray.
Then after prayers have all been said,
    We kiss goodnight—and go to bed!

What book is the father reading? Why is the Bible a special book?
How is it different from fairy-tale books?

"Thy word is true" (Psalm 119:160).

You Give Us Everlasting Life

"For God so loved the world, that he gave his only begotten Son that whosoever believeth in him should not perish, but have everlasting life" (John 3:16).

Snowman, snowman!
   Will you live for aye?
No, when the sun comes out,
   I'll surely melt away!

Little ones who love the Lord,
   Will you live for aye?
Yes, we'll live with God above
   Forever and a day!

Have you ever made a snowman? What happened to it?
Do snowmen last forever? Will those who love the Lord live forever in Heaven?

You Prepare a Place for Us in Heaven

"In my Father's house are many mansions. I go to prepare a place for you" (John 14:2).

Great Grandpa's very old today.
Today he's ninety-seven.
Mother says the time is near
When he will go to Heaven.

Angels soon will carry him
Right up to Heaven's door,
And he will have a
Happy home
In Heaven
Evermore!

Who is the birthday cake for? What will soon happen to Grandpa? Where will he have a new happy home?

You Gave Your Son to Be Our Saviour

"For God so loved the world, that he gave his only begotten Son, that whosoever believeth in him should not perish, but have everlasting life" (John 3:16).

Even a child of six or seven
   Can know the Lord, the Way to Heaven.
Even a child can know God's Word
   And answer when His voice is heard.

Come into my heart, Lord Jesus,
   And take away my sin.
I open the door, Lord Jesus,
   So come and enter in.

I know You died upon the cross,
   My sins to all forgive!
Come into my heart, Lord Jesus!
   Come into my heart to live!

Jesus said, "Behold, I stand at the door, and knock: if any man hear my voice, and open the door, I will come in to him" (Revelation 3:20).

You Shall Be Praised Each Day of the Week

"Every day will I bless thee" (Psalm 145:2)
"Daily shall he be praised" (Psalm 72:15).

I'll praise the Lord
   On SUNDAY,
As I read His Word
   And pray!

I'll praise the Lord
   On MONDAY,
As I run and skip
   And play!

I'll praise the Lord
   On TUESDAY,
      As I'm swinging
         On my swing!

I'll praise the Lord
   On WEDNESDAY,
      When I hear the
         Birdies sing!

I'll praise the Lord
On THURSDAY,
As I watch the clouds
Go by!

I'll praise the Lord
On FRIDAY,
When a rainbow's
In the sky!

I'll praise the Lord
On SATURDAY,
Just as I have before!

Day by day
Throughout the week,
I'll praise Him
More and
MORE!

Every day we can find something to praise God for. What day is it today? What can you praise and thank Him for?

You Are to Be Praised Forever!

"Seven times a day do I praise thee" (Psalm 119:165).

ONE, I'll praise Him! TWO, I'll praise Him! THREE, I'll praise Him...FOUR!

FIVE, I'll praise Him! SIX, I'll praise Him! SEVEN, I'll praise Him more!

EIGHT, I'll praise Him! NINE, I'll praise Him! TEN, and then...ELEVEN!

A THOUSAND TIMES I'LL PRAISE HIM

Till I'm on my way to Heaven!

"I will praise thy name for ever and ever" (Psalm 145:2).

94

Little Lips Everywhere Shall Bless You, Lord!

"Be thankful unto him, and bless his name" (Psalm 100:4).

  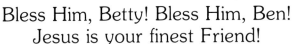  

Bless Him, Betty! Bless Him, Ben!
Jesus is your finest Friend!

Bless Him, Patty! Bless Him, Paul!
Jesus loves you one and all!

Bless Him, Sammy! Bless Him, Sue!
Jesus Christ has died for you!

Debbie. . . . . .Cindy. . . . . . Bill. . . .and Jeff!
Bless the Lord Who gives you breath!

Cathy. . . .Mary. . . . . .John. . . and Ted! Bless the Lord for daily bread!

Julie. . . . . .Bob. . . . and _____, too!
(your name)
Bless the Lord Who cares for you!

*The Bible says that everyone is to bless the Lord. When you bless God,
you are saying, "God, I thank you...I praise you...I love you!" Can you say that right now?*

My Lips Shall Praise Thee

*"Because thy lovingkindness is better than life,
my lips shall praise thee" (Psalm 63:3).*

Little lips shall praise Thee,
God in Heaven above,
Little lips shall praise Thee,
For Thy tender love.

Little lips shall whisper
Prayers on bended knee.
Little ones shall
Sing so sweetly,
"JE-SUS
LOVES
ME!"

*Can you sing "Jesus loves me"?
Is this one way your little lips can praise God?*